THE BOOK OF 1 Kings

ONE CHAPTER A DAY

GoodMorningGirls.org

The Book of 1 Kings

Welcome to Good Morning Girls! We are so glad you are joining us.

God created us to walk with Him, to know Him, and to be loved by Him. He is our living well, and when we drink from the water He continually provides, His living water will change the entire course of our lives.

Jesus said: "Whoever drinks of the water that I will give him will never be thirsty again. The water that I will give him will become in him a spring of water welling up to eternal life." ~ John 4:14 (ESV)

So let's begin.

The method we use here at GMG is called the **SOAK** method.

- ❑ **S**—The S stands for *Scripture*—Read the chapter for the day. Then choose 1-2 verses and write them out word for word. (There is no right or wrong choice— just let the Holy Spirit guide you.)

- ❑ **O**—The O stands for *Observation*—Look at the verse or verses you wrote out. Write 1 or 2 observations. What stands out to you? What do you learn about the character of God from these verses? Is there a promise, command or teaching?

- ❑ **A**—The A stands for *Application*—Personalize the verses. What is God saying to you? How can you apply them to your life? Are there any changes you need to make or an action to take?

- ❑ **K**—The K stands for *Kneeling in Prayer*—Pause, kneel and pray. Confess any sin God has revealed to you today. Praise God for His word. Pray the passage over your own life or someone you love. Ask God to help you live out your applications.

SOAK God's word into your heart and squeeze every bit of nourishment you can out of each day's scripture reading. Soon you will find your life transformed by the renewing of your mind!

Walk with the King!

Courtney

WomenLivingWell.org, GoodMorningGirls.org

Join the GMG Community

Share your daily SOAK on **Facebook.com/GoodMorningGirlsWLW**

Instagram: WomenLivingWell #GoodMorningGirls

GMG Bible Coloring Chart

COLORS	KEYWORDS
PURPLE	God, Jesus, Holy Spirit, Saviour, Messiah
PINK	women of the Bible, family, marriage, parenting, friendship, relationships
RED	love, kindness, mercy, compassion, peace, grace
GREEN	faith, obedience, growth, fruit, salvation, fellowship, repentance
YELLOW	worship, prayer, praise, doctrine, angels, miracles,power of God, blessings
BLUE	wisdom, teaching, instruction, commands
ORANGE	prophecy, history, times, places, kings, genealogies, people, numbers, covenants, vows, visions, oaths, future
BROWN/GRAY	Satan, sin, death, hell, evil, idols, false teachers, hypocrisy, temptation

Introduction to the Book of 1 Kings

As we study 1 Kings together, we will see the rise and fall of both good and bad kings, starting with David.

One of the well-known stories from this book is when God offers Solomon anything he desires, and he asks for wisdom. Solomon is given the gift of wisdom and he builds a magnificent temple for the Lord. Following this great project, Solomon falls into sin and does not end as well as he started.

Once the kingdom is divided, we see a succession of kings rising and falling as the kings go from bad to worse and commit idolatry and other evil acts. The bright lights in the midst of these dark days are the great prophets of Elijah and Elisha, who were faithful to God in all they did.

Originally, the books of 1st and 2nd Kings were one book. These books cover almost 500 years of the kingship of Israel and Judah.

The Purpose: 1 Kings gives the history of the kings and prophets of Israel and Judah.

The Author: Although the author is anonymous, tradition holds that 1 Kings was written by Jeremiah.

Time Period: This book was written around 550 B.C.

Key Verse: 1 Kings 8:23

O Lord, God of Israel, there is no God like you, in heaven above or on earth beneath, keeping covenant and showing steadfast love to your servants who walk before you with all their heart.

The Outline:

The Reign of Solomon

1. David dies and Solomon's throne is established (1-4)

2. Solomon builds the temple and his royal palace. (5-10)

3. Solomon's spiritual decline. (11)

The Kingdoms Divide

1. Jeroboam's reign of Israel (11:26-14:20)

2. Rehoboam's reign of Judah (14:21-31)

3. Abijam's reign of Judah (15:1-8)

4. Asa's reign of Judah (15:9-24)

5. Nadab's reign of Israel (15:25-32)

6. Baasha's reign of Israel (15:33-16:7)

7. Elah's reign of Israel (16:8-14)

8. Zimri's reign of Israel (16:15-20)

9. Omri's reign of Israel (16:21-28)

10. Ahab's reign of Israel (16:29-34)

Prophets and Kings

1. Ahab and Elijah (17)

2. Elijah against the Caananite Prophets (18)

3. God speaks to Elijah (19:1-18)

4. The call of Elisha (19:19-21)

5. Ahab's Misconduct (20)

6. Ahab and Jezebel's evil deeds (21)

7. Micaiah's judgement against Ahab (22:1-40)

8. Johoshaphat's reign of Judah (22:41-50)

9. Ahaziah's reign of Israel (22:51-53)

1 Kings does not just record history, it gives us lessons from history. We are going to learn many spiritual truths through the study of the kings and prophets.

Some of the chapters are quite long, so be sure to leave at least 20 minutes for your reading each day. I can't wait to see how God reveals himself personally to each of us, as we read the book of 1 Kings together, chapter by chapter. So let's get started!

Keep walking with the King!

Courtney

Now Adonijah
exalted himself, saying,
"I will be king."

1 Kings 1:5

Reflection Question:

King David's son Adonijah exalted himself to King status. Instead of waiting to be chosen as the next king, he announced his kingship. In the midst of his celebration feast, an announcement was made that King David had chosen Solomon as King. Terror struck the guests at the feast and suddenly Adonijah was fearing for his life.

God says many times in scripture that we are not to exalt ourselves but rather let God exalt us. Adonijah broke this principle and did not seek God's will for his life. Instead he recklessly went after what he wanted. Is there something in your life right now that you really want and are working hard to get? Stop and talk to God about this and write a prayer below asking God for guidance.

S—The S stands for **Scripture**

O—The O stands for **Observation**

A—The A stands for **Application**

K—The K stands for **Kneeling in Prayer**

Walk in his ways and keep his statutes

that you may prosper in all that you do.

1 Kings 2:3

Reflection Question:

David's final instructions to Solomon was a defining moment. David knew that great challenges were ahead for Solomon. In order to prosper as king, he would need to be obedient to all that God told him to do. Solomon did not always obey God but at the end of his life he said in Ecclesiastes 12:13: *"The end of the matter; all has been heard. Fear God and keep his commandments, for this is the whole duty of man."*

Solomon had learned, at the end of his life, that man must fear God and obey his commands. We must obey the Lord too. When we do not obey, it leads to extra sorrows. Our prosperity from obedience is not necessarily material but rather spiritual and eternal. In what ways have you prospered because of your obedience to God?

1 Kings 2

S—The S stands for *Scripture*

O—The O stands for *Observation*

A—The A stands for *Application*

K—The K stands for *Kneeling in Prayer*

I give you a wise and discerning mind.

1 Kings 3:12

Reflection Question:

God offered Solomon whatever he wanted and rather than asking for riches and honor and power and fame, he asked for wisdom and discernment. Solomon didn't just want knowledge in his head—he wanted understanding in his heart. God was pleased!

God cares more about our character than our possessions and popularity. If God offered to give you whatever you asked for—what would you ask for? Would God be pleased with this desire?

S—The S stands for *Scripture*

O—The O stands for *Observation*

A—The A stands for *Application*

K—The K stands for *Kneeling in Prayer*

God gave Solomon wisdom and understanding

beyond measure, and breadth of mind

like the sand on the seashore.

1 Kings 4:29

Reflection Question:

God gave Solomon wisdom. In 1 Kings 4:32 it says that Solomon spoke 3,000 Proverbs and 1,005 songs! Many of these Songs and Proverbs are found in the books of Psalms, Proverbs, Ecclesiastes and the Song of Songs.

God is still giving his people wisdom today! First, we can find it right in his Word. And then secondly, in James 1:5, it says that God gives wisdom to those who ask him for it. Is there something in your life that you need to pray and ask God to give you wisdom for? Write that prayer below?

S—The S stands for *Scripture*

O—The O stands for *Observation*

A—The A stands for *Application*

K—The K stands for *Kneeling in Prayer*

The Lord my God has given me rest on every side.

There is neither adversary nor misfortune.

1 Kings 5:4

Reflection Question:

David faced endless warfare during his reign, but God gave Solomon rest from his enemies and rest from misfortunes. With that rest, Solomon resolved to build a temple for the Lord.

Are you in a season of rest or turmoil? Perhaps the Lord is calling you to do something great for his name or perhaps he is simply calling you to stand your ground and fight the battles that are before you. What do you feel God is calling you to do in this season of life?

1 Kings 5

S—The S stands for **Scripture**

O—The O stands for **Observation**

A—The A stands for **Application**

K—The K stands for **Kneeling in Prayer**

If you will keep all my commandments

then I will establish my word with you

And I will dwell among the children of Israel

and will not forsake my people Israel.

1 Kings 6:12,13

Reflection Question:

Solomon was given a promise that if he obeyed God, God would not forsake the people of Israel and that his presence would remain with them. The very next verse says, "So Solomon built the house and finished it". The temple took seven years to build! This was not a quick and easy task, but I am sure that this promise both encouraged and comforted Solomon on weary days.

Sometimes the work God has assigned to us is difficult and long. In 1 Corinthians 6:19, it says that our bodies are the temple of the Holy Spirit and in Hebrews 13:5, we learn that God will never leave us nor forsake us. How does remembering these promises from God to you, encourage you?

1 Kings 6

S—The S stands for *Scripture*

O—The O stands for *Observation*

A—The A stands for *Application*

K—The K stands for *Kneeling in Prayer*

Solomon was building his own house thirteen years, and he finished his entire house.

1 Kings 7:1

Reflection Question:

It took Solomon 7 years to build the Lord's house and 13 years to build his own. While the temple was magnificent, it seems that Solomon wanted his own house to be even more magnificent. But one thing we must recognize is that Solomon did put building God's temple before his own and perhaps he was overly excited to get the temple into use for the people and that is why it was completed more quickly.

Sometimes we may be tempted to pursue our own personal comfort over the building of God's kingdom through evangelism and serving others. How we spend our time reveals our heart. Do you spend a lot of time on your home -- shopping and decorating and cleaning it? While this is important, we must not forget that the Lord should be first priority in our lives. Are there any changes you need to make in your life to make building God's kingdom a greater priority?

1 Kings 7

S—The S stands for *Scripture*

O—The O stands for *Observation*

A—The A stands for *Application*

K—The K stands for *Kneeling in Prayer*

Then Solomon

spread out his hands

towards heaven and said

There is no God like you,

in heaven above or on earth beneath.

1 Kings 8:22, 23

Reflection Question:

There is no God like our God! Solomon did not appoint a priest or prophet to dedicate the temple. As King, he did it himself in front of all of Israel. In verse 54 it says: *"Now as Solomon finished offering all this prayer and plea to the Lord, he arose from before the altar of the Lord, where he had knelt with hands outstretched toward heaven."* Solomon was a great King, but he never looked so great as when he kneeled before the Lord, with outstretched hands, in humble prayer.

In our culture, we teach our children to fold their hands and bow their heads in prayer. But the Old Testament tradition was to kneel down and spread out their hands towards heaven. The 4th part of the SOAK method is to "Kneel in Prayer". Is this the posture of prayer that you choose regularly? Do you lift your hands towards heaven when you kneel in prayer? Why or why no?

S—The S stands for *Scripture*

O—The O stands for *Observation*

A—The A stands for *Application*

K—The K stands for *Kneeling in Prayer*

Walk before me

with integrity of heart and uprightness,

doing according to all

that I have commanded you.

1 Kings 9:4

Reflection Question:

When Solomon completed the building of the temple and his palace, God appeared to him a second time. God answered his dedication prayer with a condition. If Solomon obeyed the Lord, he would be blessed but if he and the people of Israel did not, he was warned that this house would become a heap of ruins.

God told Solomon to walk upright as David did. We all know that David failed in various ways to obey the Lord, but David had a humble heart of repentance. God did not demand perfection from Solomon, and he does not demand perfection of us. Because of Christ's blood shed on the cross, humble obedience is not out of reach but there is a law in the New Testament of sowing and reaping (Galatians 6:7). Is there an area in your life where you need to work on obedience and root out any bad seeds you have been sowing?

S—The S stands for *Scripture*

O—The O stands for *Observation*

A—The A stands for *Application*

K—The K stands for *Kneeling in Prayer*

Happy are your men!

Happy are your servants,

who continually stand before you

and hear your wisdom!

1 Kings 10:8

Reflection Question:

The Queen of Sheba remarked on how happy Solomon's servants were because they were continually around Solomon's wisdom. While it must have been wonderful to have such a great wise king, it is even a happier thing to serve the King of Kings - Jesus!

Do you realize what a great advantage it is to have the wisdom of God's Word and the ability to be around wise people in the family of God? Sometimes we take for granted how blessed we are to have such great wisdom. Do others see your happiness that comes from being a servant of the King of Kings? Why or why not?

1 Kings 10

S—The S stands for *Scripture*

O—The O stands for *Observation*

A—The A stands for *Application*

K—The K stands for *Kneeling in Prayer*

Solomon did what was evil

in the sight of the Lord and

did not wholly follow the Lord.

1 Kings 11:6

Reflection Question:

Unbelievable! Solomon in all of his wisdom, who built the extravagant temple for the Lord and had two appearances from God himself—married foreign women and turned into a fool - worshipping pagan gods. Watching the fall of this great man is painful. Sin brought ruin to his kingdom and family dynasty. Sin ruins the honor of great men and ruins their families.

We assume that we will be wiser as we age, but Solomon was wiser in his youth than in his old age. Age does not automatically bring wisdom but rather it's an issue of our hearts and our obedience to God that brings wisdom. Have you seen this happen in the life of someone you know? How does watching the fall of someone else, serve as a warning to us? Is there an area in your life where sin has crept in? Name it and repent today.

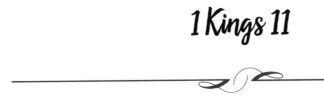

1 Kings 11

S—The S stands for **Scripture**

O—The O stands for **Observation**

A—The A stands for **Application**

K—The K stands for **Kneeling in Prayer**

But he abandoned the counsel

that the old men gave him

and took counsel with the young men

who had grown up with him.

1 Kings 12:8

Reflection Question:

Before Rehoboam had even talked with his young friends, he had already rejected the counsel of the older men. The older men encouraged him to serve the people, speak kind to the people and to lead with love. The young men gave him the opposite advice and told him to lead with fear. The older men knew the traditions of Israel and how the King affected the daily lives of the people, while the young men had grown up in the royal court and they lacked the wisdom Rehoboam needed to lead the people.

It is common for us to feel more comfortable to ask our peers for advice than an older woman, but we are missing out on the rich wisdom older women have to offer us. Do you more commonly look to your peers for advice or older women? Name some older women that you know you could go to if you were in need of advice?

1 Kings 12

S—The S stands for *Scripture*

O—The O stands for *Observation*

A—The A stands for *Application*

K—The K stands for *Kneeling in Prayer*

A lion met him on the road.

1 Kings 13:24

Reflection Question:

The prophet started out well, obeying God's commands. But then he chose to listen to a lie that directly violated the command he had from God and it ended in his death. God used a lion to judge the prophet for his disobedience. The lion killed him but did not eat the prophet's body nor the body of the donkey, to show that this was punishment from God and not simply a hungry lion.

I'm so thankful God does not put a lion in our path when we disobey him—aren't you? We see here yet again a man who starts out well but does not finish well. In the end, there's a donkey and a lion left—and both of these represent the two choices the man had. He could listen to the lion of Judah, God, and obey his word, or be stubborn and foolish like a donkey. His dead body was evidence of his wrong choice. In what ways are you tempted to doubt God's Word or listen to the lies of this world over the Word of God? I'm so thankful for God's grace, but how serious is it that we obey God.

S—The S stands for *Scripture*

O—The O stands for *Observation*

A—The A stands for *Application*

K—The K stands for *Kneeling in Prayer*

They provoked God

to jealousy with their sins.

1 Kings 14:22

Reflection Question:

Rehoboam, the son of Solomon, reigned in Judah and instead of worshiping in the magnificent temple that his father had built, he built high places to worship idols on every hill and under every tree! This act of great defiance provoked God to jealousy. God's jealousy was not the sin of envy but rather he was jealous for what belonged to him, like an adulterous wife provokes her husband by her unfaithfulness.

Before we are too astonished at Rehoboam's ability to so easily worship false idols, we must pause and self-reflect. Anything that we take greater pleasure or security in than God is an idol. Identify some of the idols you see in the culture around you. Which of these idols do you need to be on guard against in your own life?

S—The S stands for **Scripture**

O—The O stands for **Observation**

A—The A stands for **Application**

K—The K stands for **Kneeling in Prayer**

Asa did what was right

in the eyes of the Lord.

1 Kings 15:11

Reflection Question:

Corruption had spread in the land of Judah before the reign of Asa. When Asa became king, he removed the idols from the land. All of the kings were usually measured against David's heart. David was Asa's great-great-grandfather and Asa was compared to David as one who did what was right in God's eyes. Asa did not have the same talents of music and poetry and military victory, but he had a heart that desired to do what was right.

Sometimes we are tempted to compare our lives with, but God did not give us all the same talents and abilities. What he is looking for most is a heart that desires to do what is right. If a story was being written about your life, would the author say these words about you, "she did what was right in the eyes of the Lord." Why or why not?

S—The S stands for **Scripture**

O—The O stands for **Observation**

A—The A stands for **Application**

K—The K stands for **Kneeling in Prayer**

Ahab did evil in the sight of the Lord,

more than all who were before him.

1 Kings 16:30

Reflection Question:

Ahab was the most evil king Israel had ever seen. Ahab served and worshiped Baal and was displeasing to the Lord. Essentially, he was a "drama king" as we will see in further passages.

One thing we learn from both the good and bad kings of Israel, is what God requires of leaders. We can see what pleased the Lord and what displeased the Lord. Are you a leader? No matter who you are, you have a sphere of influence. Who is in your sphere of influence and are you pleasing the Lord in the way you lead and influence others?

1 Kings 16

S—The S stands for **Scripture**

O—The O stands for **Observation**

A—The A stands for **Application**

K—The K stands for **Kneeling in Prayer**

The jar of flour was not spent,

neither did the jug of oil become empty,

according to the word of the Lord

that he spoke by Elijah.

1 Kings 17:16

Reflection Question:

Elijah obeyed the Lord and was in the center of God's will, and yet his brook dried up. But God used that to direct him to the widow's house. He went without questioning God and he instructed the widow to make him bread. The widow took great risk and did as he asked and God fulfilled his promise to the widow, her son and Elijah. She ate for many days and her flour and oil did not run out.

God uses the most unlikely people to show his glory. God used the widow's faith to show himself as a provider, as he supplied her needs and the needs of Elijah. Notice that the miracle only came after she prepared the meal for Elijah. Is there something in your life that God is asking you to do that requires risk? What is keeping you from stepping out in faith.

S—The S stands for *Scripture*

O—The O stands for *Observation*

A—The A stands for *Application*

K—The K stands for *Kneeling in Prayer*

How long will you go limping

between two different opinions?

If the Lord is God, follow him.

1 Kings 18:21

Reflection Question:

I love this story! When the One True God was up against the false god, named Baal—God prevailed. There was no voice and no answer from the false God. Then fire rained down on Elijah's altar and when all the people saw it, they fell on their faces and declared, "The Lord he is God". There is no God like our God!

Before the fire rained down from heaven, Elijah called on the people to stop wavering between God and Baal. Do you feel at times torn between God's ways and the worlds ways? Would you have had the courage and faith in God to do what Elijah did? How does Elijah's faith and God's display of strength encourage you to not waver in your devotion to God?

S—The S stands for **Scripture**

O—The O stands for **Observation**

A—The A stands for **Application**

K—The K stands for **Kneeling in Prayer**

The Lord was not in the wind.

The Lord was not in the earthquake.

The Lord was not in the fire.

(He was in) the sound of a low whisper.

(Based on) 1 Kings 19:11 & 12

Reflection Question:

Elijah was discouraged and so the Lord wanted to speak to him. But God showed Elijah that he was not in his large displays of power. He was not in the wind. He was not in the earthquake. He was not in the fire but rather in the stillness. In the quiet, God whispered to Elijah.

While God shows himself to us in his mighty power, displayed through creation, that is not always the way God reveals himself. Sometimes we may be tempted to look for God to display himself through mighty acts that everyone can see. But God often comes to us in a soft whisper. Do you have trouble being still to pray, worship, and listen to God's voice? What is getting in the way of finding that quietness, so you can hear God!

1 Kings 19

S—The S stands for *Scripture*

O—The O stands for *Observation*

A—The A stands for *Application*

K—The K stands for *Kneeling in Prayer*

I will give all this great multitude

into your hand,

and you shall know

that I am the Lord.

1 Kings 20:28

Reflection Question:

The Syrians said that the Lord is God of the hills but not the God of the valley and God took great offense to their bad theology. God punished them by giving Israel a great victory over them.

Man's wrong ideas about God take away from God's glory and majesty. God's power is everywhere! He can work through the most unlikely and weakest of people. What are some ideas that people have about God that you know are wrong? How have you seen God work through some of the most unlikely and weakest of people?

S—The S stands for **Scripture**

O—The O stands for **Observation**

A—The A stands for **Application**

K—The K stands for **Kneeling in Prayer**

There was none who sold himself

to do what was evil in the sight of the Lord

like Ahab, whom Jezebel his wife incited.

1 Kings 21:25

Reflection Question:

It all began when Ahab coveted his neighbor's vineyard. His own royal gardens were not enough so his wife Jezebel concocted an evil plan to take it by force. Ahab's sin was multiplied by his wife who fed his evil desires. An innocent man was murdered so he could have what he lusted after.

You may have heard the saying, "Behind every great man is a great woman." But we should consider that sometimes behind evil men...is an evil woman. Jezebel was a smart and assertive woman who used her strength for evil. Being assertive and strong are not bad qualities when they are used for the good of others. How can you use your strengths for the good of those who live in your home, your workplace and your church.

S—The S stands for **Scripture**

O—The O stands for **Observation**

A—The A stands for **Application**

K—The K stands for **Kneeling in Prayer**

Inquire first
For the word of the Lord.

1 Kings 22:5

Reflection Question:

Jehoshaphat encouraged Ahab to inquire of the Lord before going out to battle. It was common for kings to seek out prophets for direction, but Ahab had trouble finding true prophets who were faithful to the Lord and his direction.

We see that while Ahab pulled Jehoshaphat into his war, Jehosphaphat pulled Ahab into his desire to seek God first. We too need to inquire of the Lord before we begin new endeavors. Is there something new you have been thinking about starting, joining or buying? Have you asked the Lord about this yet? Take time now to write a prayer asking God for direction and guidance.

1 Kings 22

S—The S stands for **Scripture**

O—The O stands for **Observation**

A—The A stands for **Application**

K—The K stands for **Kneeling in Prayer**

Made in the USA
Columbia, SC
06 February 2020

87599061R00030